The Wednes... Wars

Gary D. Schmidt

STUDENT PACKET

NOTE:

The trade book edition of the novel used to prepare this guide is found in the Novel Units catalog and on the Novel Units website. Using other editions may have varied page references.

Please note: We have assigned Interest Levels based on our knowledge of the themes and ideas of the books included in the Novel Units sets, however, please assess the appropriateness of this novel or trade book for the age level and maturity of your students prior to reading with them. You know your students best!

SBN 978-1-60878-717-3

To order, contact your local school supply store, or:

Toll-Free Fax: 877.716.7272
Phone: 888.650.4224
3901 Union Blvd., Suite 155
St. Louis, MO 63115

sales@novelunits.com
novelunits.com

Note to the Teacher

Selected activities, quizzes, and test questions in this Novel Units® Student Packet are labeled with the following reading/language arts skills for quick reference. These skills can be found above quiz/test questions or sections and in the activity headings.

Basic Understanding: The student will demonstrate a basic understanding of written texts. The student will:
- use a text's structure or other sources to locate and recall information (Locate Information)
- determine main idea and identify relevant facts and details (Main Idea and Details)
- use prior knowledge and experience to comprehend and bring meaning to a text (Prior Knowledge)
- summarize major ideas in a text (Summarize Major Ideas)

Literary Elements: The student will apply knowledge of literary elements to understand written texts. The student will:
- analyze characters from a story (Character Analysis)
- analyze conflict and problem resolution (Conflict/Resolution)
- recognize and interpret literary devices (flashback, foreshadowing, symbolism, simile, metaphor, etc.) (Literary Devices)
- consider characters' points of view (Point of View)
- recognize and analyze a story's setting (Setting)
- understand and explain themes in a text (Theme)

Analyze Written Texts: The student will use a variety of strategies to analyze written texts. The student will:
- identify the author's purpose (Author's Purpose)
- identify cause and effect relationships in a text (Cause/Effect)
- identify characteristics representative of a given genre (Genre)
- interpret information given in a text (Interpret Text)
- make and verify predictions with information from a text (Predictions)
- sequence events in chronological order (Sequencing)
- identify and use multiple text formats (Text Format)
- follow written directions and write directions for others to follow (Follow/Write Directions)

Critical Thinking: The student will apply critical-thinking skills to analyze written texts. The student will:
- write and complete analogies (Analogies)
- find similarities and differences throughout a text (Compare/Contrast)
- draw conclusions from information given (Drawing Conclusions)
- make and explain inferences (Inferences)
- respond to texts by making connections and observations (Making Connections)
- recognize and identify the mood of a text (Mood)
- recognize an author's style and how it affects a text (Style)
- support responses by referring to relevant aspects of a text (Support Responses)
- recognize and identify the author's tone (Tone)
- write to entertain, such as through humorous poetry or short stories (Write to Entertain)
- write to express ideas (Write to Express)
- write to inform (Write to Inform)
- write to persuade (Write to Persuade)
- demonstrate understanding by creating visual images based on text descriptions (Visualizing)
- practice math skills as they relate to a text (Math Skills)

Name _____

I Predict...

Directions: Spend a few minutes looking at the cover of the novel and flipping through its pages. What can you predict about the characters, the setting, and the problem in the novel? Write your predictions in the spaces below.

The Characters	The Setting	The Problem

From the information you gathered above, do you think you will enjoy reading this novel? Circle your response on the scale below.

Explain your prediction on the lines below.

0 —— 1 —— 2 —— 3 —— 4 —— 5 —— 6 —— 7 —— 8 —— 9 —— 10

I will not like this novel.   I will really like this novel.

_____

_____

_____

_____

_____

Name _____

Anticipation and Reaction

Directions: Consider the following statements before you read the novel. Place a checkmark in one of the boxes to show whether you agree or disagree with each statement, and provide your reasoning. After you have completed the novel, mark your response again. On a separate sheet of paper, provide explanations for each of your opinions that have changed.

Response Before Reading	Statement	Response After Reading
☑ you agree ☐ you disagree	1. During wartime, everyone should support the government.	☐ you agree ☐ you disagree
☑ you agree ☐ you disagree	2. Shakespeare is boring and irrelevant to us today.	☐ you agree ☐ you disagree
☐ you agree ☑ you disagree	3. Power and money are more important than love.	☐ you agree ☐ you disagree
☐ you agree ☑ you disagree	4. Rats make good pets.	☐ you agree ☐ you disagree
☐ you agree ☑ you disagree	5. First impressions are always accurate.	☐ you agree ☐ you disagree
☑ you agree *w/reservations* ☐ you disagree	6. Teachers are not interested in the personal lives of their students.	☐ you agree ☐ you disagree
☐ you agree ☑ you disagree	7. Children should always agree with their parents.	☐ you agree ☐ you disagree

Name _____

Vocabulary Card Game

Teacher Directions:
- Photocopy and cut out the following vocabulary cards.
- If necessary, divide the class into groups.
- Give one card to each student in the class/group.
- The student who has the starred card begins by reading his/her question.
- The student who has the card with the correct vocabulary word responds and then reads his/her question.
- Play continues in this manner until all cards have been read.

☆ **parishioners**	**mutilation**
Who has a word that means irreparable damage?	Who has a word that means shifting back and forth?

alternating	**ally**
Who has a word that means friend or supporter?	Who has a word that means a large store that offers a wide variety of goods?

emporium	**recruited**
Who has a word that means enrolled or enlisted?	Who has a word that means the outer boundary?

perimeter	foil
Who has a word that means to prevent someone's success?	Who has a word that means the act of driving something forward?

propulsion	accomplice
Who has a word that means a co-conspirator in crime?	Who has a word that means failing to provide proper care?

negligent	mooring
Who has a word that means securing a boat or ship to one place?	Who has a word that means residents of a religious community?

© Novel Units, Inc.

Name _____

Vocabulary Cloze

vile	quivering	reckon	unbecoming
equation	circulate	expel	presume
rioted	remnants	mercy	

Directions: Fill in the blanks below with the correct vocabulary words.

Charlie sat in his seat, anxiously waiting for Ms. Zartik to distribute the math tests.

Last night, he dreamt his class (1) _____ against all math tests, holding

signs and running wild in the school's halls. This morning he had to face reality and take

the despicable, (2) _____ test, solving every (3) _____

correctly. As Charlie began to write, he tried to steady his (4) _____

hand. Ms. Zartik began to (5) _____ around the classroom, looking

over shoulders and making sure everyone had their eyes on their own papers. "I

(6) _____ everyone knows that if you are caught cheating, you

automatically fail," she reminded the class. My classmate Brittany chewed on her pencil

nervously, as was her (7) _____ habit. I wondered if Ms. Zartik would

just (8) _____ me from school; then I wouldn't have to take any tests.

As I finished, I felt the (9) _____ of anxiety fade away and believed

Ms. Zartik would have (10) _____ on me when grading my exam.

"Could you please grade this now?" I asked as I turned it in. Ms. Zartik picked up her red

pen. As she finished, she paused to (11) _____ my score. I saw her write

a big "A" at the top of the page. I breathed a sigh of relief as I collapsed into my desk chair

and smiled.

Name _____

Vocabulary Matching

rhythm	devious	jesting	swathe
coagulated	advance	virtue	rivalry
vandals	seclusion	menorah	exquisite
vocation	corresponding	bribe	suspicion
insubstantial	revels	careened	crooning

Directions: Match each vocabulary word to the correct definition.

_____ 1. rhythm

_____ 2. devious

_____ 3. jesting

_____ 4. swathe

_____ 5. coagulated

_____ 6. advance

_____ 7. virtue

_____ 8. rivalry

_____ 9. vandals

_____ 10. seclusion

_____ 11. menorah

_____ 12. exquisite

_____ 13. vocation

_____ 14. corresponding

_____ 15. bribe

_____ 16. suspicion

_____ 17. insubstantial

_____ 18. revels

_____ 19. careened

_____ 20. crooning

a. ribbon; band

b. payment ahead of time

c. admirable quality

d. funny; amusing

e. people who willfully destroy others' property

f. thickened; stopped bleeding

g. nine-branched candleholder used on Hanukkah

h. patterned repetition of formal elements

i. beautiful; extraordinary

j. feeling of mistrust or doubt

k. dishonest; indirect

l. competition

m. not existing in reality

n. isolation from others; solitude

o. murmured; smooth; soft

p. promise something to persuade someone

q. moved forward at high speed

r. occupation; profession

s. noisy festivities; merrymaking

t. assigned to handle communications

Name _____

Vocabulary Crossword Puzzle

splayed	impressive	intercepted	ample
nifty	fortifying	consonant	heath
eaves	thermal	vengeance	component
aerial	caches		

Directions: Using the vocabulary words above, create a crossword puzzle answer key by filling in the grid below. Then, write clues to the crossword puzzle. Number the clues to match the numbers in the squares. The teacher will give each student a blank grid. Make a blank copy of your crossword puzzle for other students to answer. Exchange your clues with someone else, and solve the blank puzzle s/he gives you. Check the completed puzzles with the answer keys.

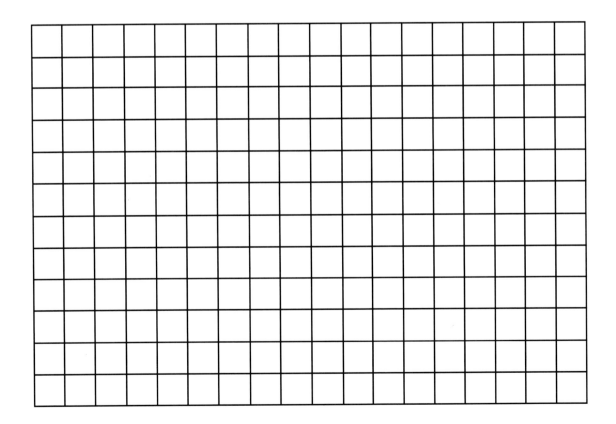

Vocabulary Analogies

dank	lapel	prosperous	tragic
eternal	arrogant	unsavory	allotted
procedural	begrudge		

Directions: Complete the analogies below.

1. _____ is to INDEFINITE as TEMPORARY is to BRIEF.

2. CONSIDERATE is to SELFISH as MODEST is to _____.

3. UNUSUAL is to UNCOMMON as _____ is to ROUTINE.

4. CUFF is to PANT as _____ is to COAT.

5. FAIR is to UNJUST as HONORABLE is to _____.

6. RESENT is to _____ as REVEAL is to EXPOSE.

7. JOYFUL is to HAPPY as _____ is to SAD.

8. MONEY is to _____ as DISTINCTION is to FAMOUS.

9. HUMID is to MUGGY as _____ is to CLAMMY.

10. ALLOWED is to PERMITTED as PREARRANGED is to _____.

Name _____

Vocabulary Word Exchange

refuse	unalloyed	underestimated	stance
unscathed	diction	dispense	demean
vanquished	dispatch	allusion	arteries
commuters	humane	contour	improper
scaffolding	levitate	brittle	

Directions: Choose 12 vocabulary words from above to write in the boxes below. For each word, write one correct and one incorrect definition. (Make sure the incorrect definitions are reasonable.) Exchange sheets with a partner, and have him or her choose the correct definition in each row. Check your partner's answers.

Vocabulary Word	Definition #1	Definition #2
1.		
2.		
3.		
4.		
5.		
6.		
7.		
8.		
9.		
10.		
11.		
12.		

Name _____

Vocabulary Multiple Choice

incinerated	rafters	renovate	extremity
tsar	synagogue	congregation	outskirts
abolitionist	incense	melancholy	combustion

Directions: Select the word that best defines the vocabulary word as it is used in the novel.

_____ 1. **incinerated** a. burned to ashes   b. blown away   c. frozen solid

_____ 2. **rafters** a. tiles   b. beams   c. pipes

_____ 3. **renovate** a. observe   b. remodel   c. landscape

_____ 4. **extremity** a. exaggeration   b. strategy   c. surprise

_____ 5. **tsar** a. ruler   b. plague   c. war

_____ 6. **synagogue** a. cemetery   b. temple   c. school

_____ 7. **congregation** a. parishioners   b. clergy   c. administration

_____ 8. **outskirts** a. midpoints   b. interiors   c. boundaries

_____ 9. **abolitionist** a. government-funded   b. inner-city   c. equal-rights

_____ 10. **incense** a. split wood   b. burning candles   c. fragrant substance

_____ 11. **melancholy** a. interested   b. gloomy   c. confused

_____ 12. **combustion** a. burning   b. noise   c. wreckage

Name _____

Vocabulary Fill-in

comedy	nomination	taunted	heaved
resin	climax	latrines	repellant
sponsored	yarmulka		

A. Directions: Fill in the blanks below with the correct vocabulary words.

1. The student's family _____ the French exchange student.

2. His education reached its _____ when he graduated from college.

3. The boys were admonished after they _____ a girl who tripped.

4. The mosquitoes continued to bite me even after I sprayed myself with insect

   _____.

5. All of the Jewish men wore a(n) _____ to the wedding ceremony.

6. After a week of camping, we decided to designate a new place for the _____.

7. In theater, a play is often categorized as a tragedy or a(n) _____.

8. After trimming the trees in the backyard, my hands were covered in sticky cedar

   _____.

9. He _____ his plastic rifle through the air during the drill performance.

10. The _____ of the candidates brought excitement to the city.

B. Directions: Using the vocabulary words above, write two sentences of your own. Each sentence should contain two vocabulary words. Do not use the same word more than once.

_____

_____

_____

_____

_____

_____

Directions: Answer the following questions on a separate sheet of paper. Use your answers in class discussions, for writing assignments, and to review for tests.

September

1. Where does Holling attend school?
2. Whom does Holling consider to be a troublemaker?
3. Where do Holling and his family attend worship services?
4. How does Holling refer to his house?
5. Why does Holling search for an "ally"?
6. Why does Holling's father insist that Holling get along with Mrs. Baker?
7. What seems to be one of Holling's favorite books?
8. Why do the seventh-grade classrooms have a Coat Room instead of lockers?
9. Why does Meryl Lee get mad at Holling after she looks in his desk?
10. Whom does Holling injure during the soccer game at recess?
11. How does Mrs. Baker try to escape having to stay late on Wednesdays?
12. What announcement does Mr. Guareschi make regarding Mrs. Baker's husband?

October

1. Why does Mai Thi go to Catechism even though she is not Catholic?
2. What does Mrs. Baker have Holling do on Wednesday afternoons?
3. What are the dozen trays of cream puffs for?
4. Why do Holling's classmates threaten him?
5. How are the cream puffs ruined?
6. What does Holling's sister paint on her cheek?
7. For what prestigious position is Holling's father a candidate?
8. Why does Holling's sister want to be a flower child?
9. What does Mrs. Baker start teaching Holling on Wednesday afternoons?
10. Who are Sycorax and Caliban?
11. How did Mrs. Baker get Sycorax and Caliban?
12. Where do Sycorax and Caliban go after they escape from their cages?
13. What Shakespeare play does Holling begin to read?

14. Which character in *The Merchant of Venice* do Mrs. Baker and Holling agree is not really a villain?

November

1. What happens in the "Perfect Living Room" (p. 49)?
2. What does Holling like most about *The Tempest*?
3. Which curse does Holling perfect first?
4. Which position does Miss Violet have Holling sing in Chorus?
5. Why does Miss Violet call on Meryl Lee during class?
6. What does Holling remember as he passes a window filled with cream puffs?
7. What puts Holling's father in a good mood?
8. What does Mr. Goldman tell Holling he needs?
9. How much does Holling pay for the two dozen cream puffs?
10. What happens to the cream puffs Holling brings for the class?
11. What must Holling wear as part of his Shakespearean costume?
12. How does Mrs. Baker "show mercy" to Holling?
13. What does Mrs. Baker tell Holling that defeat can do?
14. What happened to Mrs. Bigio's husband?

December

1. Which two holiday symbols decorate the school's lobby?
2. Why does Mr. Hoodhood encourage Holling to wear the yellow tights?
3. Which baseball player is coming to the Baker Sporting Emporium?
4. What is happening the same night as the baseball player's autograph signing?
5. Why don't Holling's parents attend his Shakespeare performance?
6. How do Danny, Meryl Lee, and Mai Thi react to Holling's performance?
7. Why does the bus driver take Holling to the Emporium?
8. What does the bus driver give Holling?
9. Why doesn't the baseball player sign Holling's baseball?
10. How does Danny react to the baseball player's treatment of Holling?
11. Why doesn't Holling complain about Mrs. Bigio's cooking?

12. Why is Mrs. Bigio especially mean to Mai Thi one day?

13. What does Mrs. Baker give Danny, Doug, and Holling after school?

14. What do Mrs. Baker and her brother-in-law arrange for Danny, Doug, and Holling?

January

1. Whose picture is on the cover of the newspaper on New Year's Day?

2. How did Doug Swieteck get a black eye?

3. Where else besides Holling's school does Doug Swieteck's brother post the newspaper photos?

4. What new contract is Holling's father now trying to obtain?

5. Why doesn't Holling's sister want him to go to military school?

6. What does Mrs. Baker teach Holling from *Macbeth*?

7. Why doesn't Mr. Guareschi cancel school when it snows and the roads are icy?

8. Why must the students wear their coats in class and sit in half-dark classrooms?

9. Who gives Mai Thi a cup of hot chocolate?

10. Whom does Holling hit with a snowball?

11. Whom does Holling encounter in the bathroom?

12. Why does Holling get hit by a bus?

13. Who takes Holling to the hospital?

14. What is posted throughout the school the day Holling returns?

February

1. What do Holling and his sister complain about wearing for their father's ceremony?

2. What unfortunate event happens before Holling and his family leave for the ceremony?

3. What does Holling become concerned with in his classroom?

4. How does Mrs. Baker describe *Romeo and Juliet*?

5. Whom does Holling invite on a date for Valentine's Day?

6. What word does Holling use to describe his father's design for the new junior high?

7. Where is Danny taking Mai Thi for Valentine's Day?

8. What does Mrs. Baker tell Holling is more important than how much he spends on Meryl Lee?

Name _____

9. What does Mrs. Bigio give Holling for his date with Meryl Lee?
10. What word describes Mr. Kowalski's design for the new junior high school?
11. In what way did Mr. Kowalski change his design for the new school?
12. Why does Holling leave the board meeting?
13. What company withdraws its bid for the new junior high school?
14. What news does Mrs. Baker receive about her husband?

March

1. Where are the Vietcong intensifying their attacks on American soldiers?
2. What does Holling help Mr. Vendleri with in Mrs. Baker's classroom?
3. When are the school board members coming to observe Mrs. Baker?
4. Who is the track coach at Camillo Junior High?
5. Why does Holling decide to run on the weekend?
6. How does Mrs. Baker help prepare Holling for cross-country tryouts?
7. To whom does Mrs. Baker compare Holling when he begins to run better?
8. What code words does Holling think Mrs. Baker should use to tell students they have done well?
9. What award does Holling discover Mrs. Baker received in the past?
10. What does Mrs. Baker believe Shakespeare's writings are about?
11. What does Mrs. Baker say to Holling after he recites Shakespeare for the school board members?
12. What ruins Mrs. Baker's class lecture on the day of the school board observation?
13. Who delivers the rats to their cage?
14. What is the "Big M," according to Coach Quatrini?
15. Why does Holling run extraordinarily fast during his tryout?
16. What special dessert does Mrs. Bigio make for Mrs. Baker's class?

Name _____

April

1. Who had the fastest time during cross-country tryouts?

2. What is the American operation to relieve the Marines and find missing American soldiers at Khesanh called?

3. Why does Holling's sister believe President Johnson is not running for reelection?

4. Where is Meryl Lee's family planning to move?

5. Why does Holling run behind the eighth graders during practice?

6. What project are Holling and Meryl Lee working on together?

7. Where is Holling when he hears that Martin Luther King, Jr. has been assassinated?

8. What time is Holling's father supposed to pick him up from school on Opening Day at Yankee Stadium?

9. Why does Holling believe his father will not be taking him to the Yankees game?

10. What do Holling, Danny, and Doug do after the Yankees game?

11. Why do the Yankees players recognize Mrs. Baker?

12. Whom does Mrs. Baker stay at the Stadium to meet?

13. Who is Holling's sister's new friend?

14. Where does Holling's sister want to go to college? What does her father want for her?

15. What happens to Danny after he takes the lead in the cross-country meet?

16. What motivates Holling to pass the eighth graders during his race?

May

1. Why is May an important month at Camillo Junior High?

2. Which local architecture firm will renovate Yankee Stadium?

3. What new car does Holling's father purchase?

4. With whom does Holling's sister leave home?

5. How do Holling, Meryl Lee, and Mai Thi help Danny?

6. Why doesn't Holling want to be called Mr. Hoodhood?

7. Where do Mrs. Baker and Holling go on a field trip?

8. What do Holling and Mrs. Baker do together in Saint Adelbert's?

9. What does Holling say is the main reason the house feels empty?

10. How much money will it cost Holling's sister to take a bus back to New York City?

11. How much money does Holling get from his savings bond?

12. Whom does Holling ask to pick up his sister from the Port Authority? What is their answer?

13. Why does Holling take his father's car keys?

14. Who takes Holling to the bus station?

15. What does Holling say his sister found on her journey?

16. What are the first two words of Mrs. Baker's telegram?

June

1. What outdoor activity does Mrs. Baker dislike?

2. How did Lieutenant Baker survive after his helicopter was shot down?

3. What genre is *Much Ado About Nothing*?

4. What happens to Robert Kennedy?

5. Where do Holling and Heather go for comfort after Kennedy is shot?

6. What happens to the cans of chili and utensils in Holling's pack?

7. What does Mrs. Sidman do that scares the students?

8. What spoils the students' first night camping?

9. What do the students do for most of the day after their sleepless night?

10. What follows Doug back to the campsite from the latrine?

11. What does Mrs. Bigio bring with her to the campsite?

12. What does Mrs. Bigio offer Mai Thi?

13. How does Holling feel about Danny's bar mitzvah?

14. In what way does Holling stand up to his father?

15. To which character in Shakespeare does Mrs. Baker compare Holling at the end of the novel?

16. What are Mrs. Baker's students holding when Lieutenant Baker arrives home?

Name _____

Story Map

Directions: Fill in each box below with information about the novel.

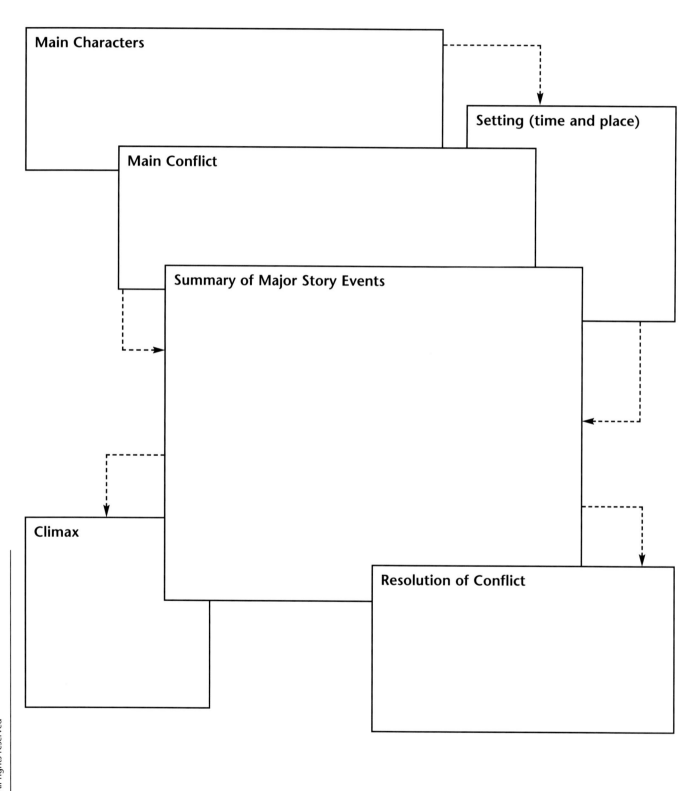

Main Characters

Setting (time and place)

Main Conflict

Summary of Major Story Events

Climax

Resolution of Conflict

Name _____

Understanding Values

Values represent people's beliefs about what is important, good, or worthwhile. For example, most families value spending time together.

Directions: Think about the following characters from the novel and the values they exhibit. What do they value? What beliefs do they have about what is important, good, or worthwhile? On the chart below, list each character's three most important values, from most important to least. Be prepared to share your lists during a class discussion.

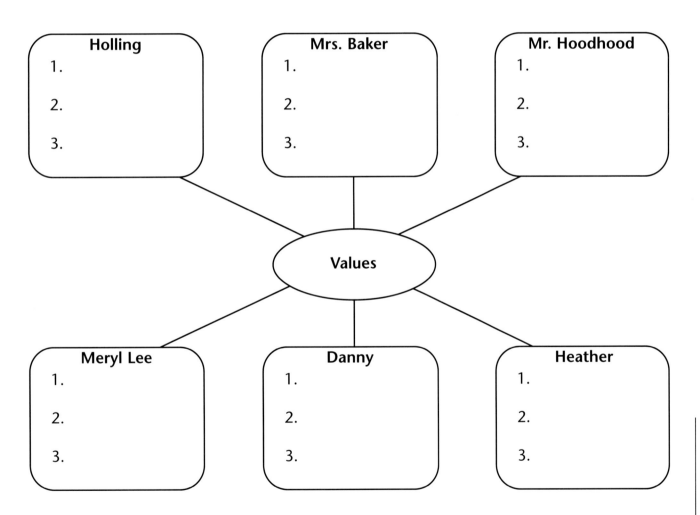

After you have finished the chart and participated in the class discussion, think about which character seems to have values most like your own. Write a paragraph that explains why you chose this character.

Name _____

Qualities of a Hero

Directions: Choose a character from the novel. For each quality listed in the left column, tell if the character has this quality. If you write "yes" in the second column, then you must list an event in the third column that proves that the character has the quality. If you write "no" in the second column, you may leave the third column blank.

Quality	Does the character have this quality? (yes or no)	Event from the Story
honest		
fair		
brave		
kind		
smart		
good friend		

Look at the chart you filled in above. Based on this information, do you think the character is a hero? Explain your decision on the lines below.

_____

_____

_____

_____

_____

| © Novel Units, Inc.

Name _____

Conflict

The **conflict** of a story is the struggle between two people or two forces. There are three main types of conflict: person vs. person, person vs. nature or society, and person vs. self.

Directions: The characters experience some conflicts in the story. In the chart below, list the names of three major characters. In the space provided, list a conflict each character experiences. Then, explain how each conflict is resolved in the story.

Character:

Conflict	Resolution

Character:

Conflict	Resolution

Character:

Conflict	Resolution

Attribute Web

Directions: Identify six characters from the novel, and place them on the long spokes of the web. On the shorter lines, list three traits that describe each character.

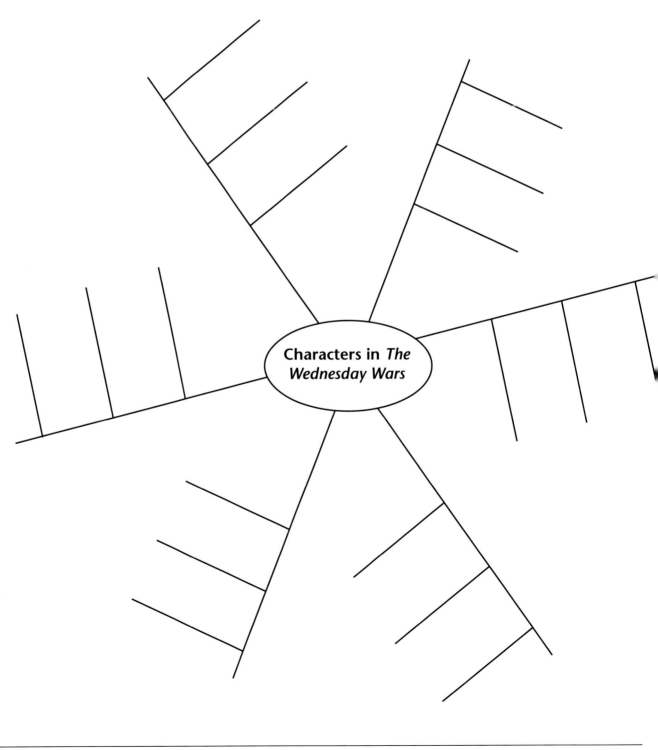

Name _____

Effects of Reading

Directions: When reading, each part of a novel may affect you in a different way. Think about how parts of the novel affected you in different ways. Did some parts make you laugh? cry? want to do something to help someone? Below, list one part of the novel that touched each of the following parts of the body: your head (made you think), your heart (made you feel), your funny bone (made you laugh), or your feet (spurred you to action).

Your head	Your heart

Your funny bone	Your feet

Name _____

Characterization

Characterization is the portrayal of an imaginary person by what he says or does, by what others say about him or how they react to him, and by what the author reveals directly or through a narrator.

Directions: Fill in the chart below with information about a specific character. Think about why s/he acts and speaks as s/he does, and what traits these actions and words reveal.

Character:

Actions/Words	Reason	Trait	Narrator's Comments

Name _____

Decision-making Grid

Directions: The decision-making grid below is supposed to make it easier to find the best solution to a problem. Fill in criterion #3 with another question you believe is important to ask when making a decision. Then, complete the grid. Choose a solution, and write a paragraph explaining the reasons behind your choice.

State the problem: Holling's sister wants to come home, but she does not have money and cannot ask her parents for help.	**Criterion #1** Will the solution hurt someone?	**Criterion #2** Will it make me feel better?	**Criterion #3**
Solution #1:			
Solution #2:			
Solution #3:			
Solution #4:			

Sequence

Directions: Identify six major events in the novel, and list them below in sequential order.

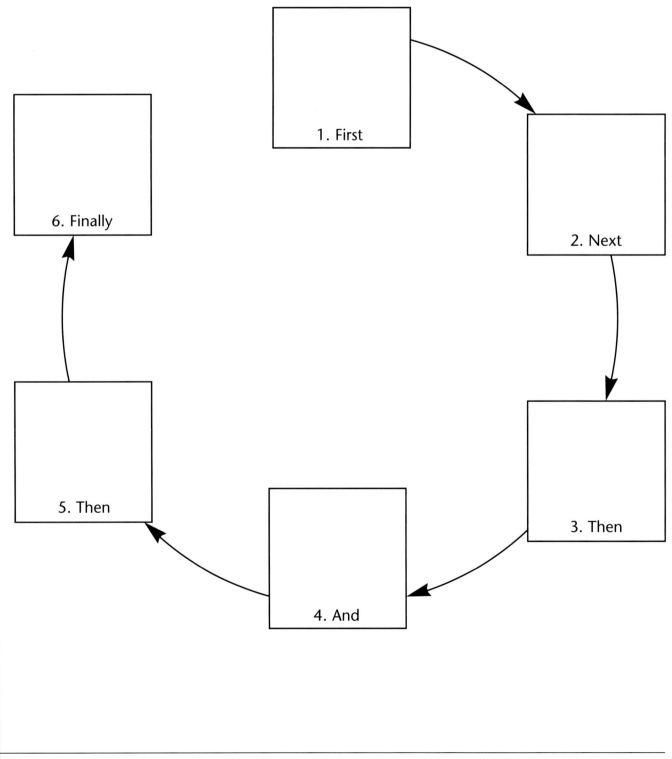

Name _____

Thematic Analysis

Directions: Choose a theme from the novel to be the focus of your word web. On the spokes, provide examples from the novel that support the theme. Then, answer the question in each starred box.

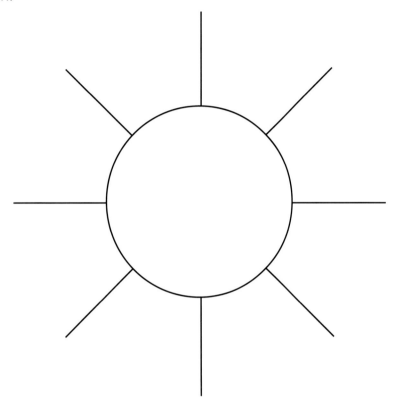

 What is the author's main message?

 What did you learn from the novel?

(Literary Elements)
A. Graphic Organizer: Complete the story map below.

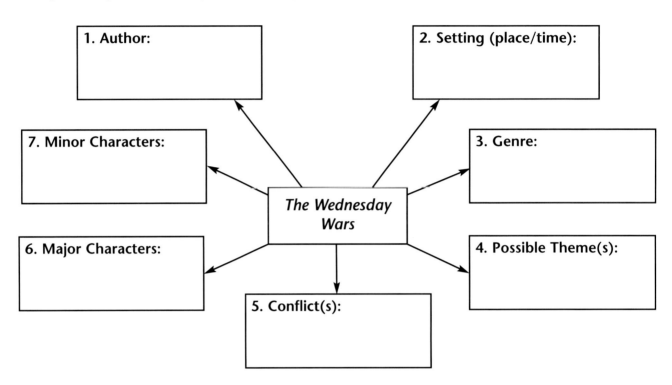

1. Author:

2. Setting (place/time):

7. Minor Characters:

3. Genre:

The Wednesday Wars

6. Major Characters:

4. Possible Theme(s):

5. Conflict(s):

(Main Idea and Details)
B. True/False: Mark each with a *T* for true or an *F* for false.

____ 8. Holling believes his teacher, Mrs. Baker, dislikes him.

____ 9. During recess, Doug Swieteck's brother trips Holling.

____ 10. Mrs. Baker's husband will soon be deployed to Vietnam.

____ 11. Holling intentionally covers the first batch of cream puffs in chalk dust.

____ 12. Holling's father owns a bakery.

____ 13. Meryl Lee is from Vietnam.

____ 14. Sycorax and Caliban escape when Mrs. Baker tries to clean their cage.

____ 15. Holling agrees to perform in a Shakespeare play in order to get a discount on cream puffs.

____ 16. Holling must wear bright red tights in the play.

____ 17. Mrs. Bigio's husband is killed in Vietnam.

(Drawing Conclusions)
C. Open-Ended Comprehension: On a separate sheet of paper, explain how the war in Vietnam affects Holling's story.

Name _____

A. Multiple Choice: Choose the BEST answer.

(Main Idea and Details)

____ 1. Which person does NOT attend Holling's Shakespeare performance?
   a. Danny
   b. Mai Thi
   c. Mr. Hoodhood
   d. Mrs. Baker

(Cause/Effect)

____ 2. Mickey Mantle does not autograph Holling's baseball because Holling
   a. is late
   b. talks too much
   c. is wearing tights
   d. forgot to bring his baseball

(Inferences)

____ 3. Mrs. Baker arranges for Holling, Doug, and Danny to meet Joe Pepitone and Horace Clarke in order to
   a. bribe the boys to stay after class and clean erasers
   b. apologize for encouraging Holling to be in the play
   c. make up for the terrible meals Mrs. Bigio is serving
   d. reward the boys for their noble behavior and loyalty

(Cause/Effect)

____ 4. When Doug will not help him cut out Holling's newspaper photos, Doug Swieteck's brother
   a. hits Doug
   b. gives up on the project
   c. elicits help from Danny
   d. promises to take revenge on Doug

(Cause/Effect)

____ 5. As revenge against Doug Swieteck's brother, Holling
   a. pushes him in the hall
   b. hits him with a snowball
   c. reports him to Mr. Guareschi
   d. threatens him in the boys' restroom

Name _____

(Inferences)

_____ 6. Mrs. Bigio does not offer Mai Thi hot chocolate because Mai Thi
   a. is mad at her
   b. is Vietnamese
   c. insulted her cooking
   d. does not like hot chocolate

(Drawing Conclusions)

_____ 7. Holling's father does not go to the hospital when Holling is hit by a bus because
   a. the roads are icy
   b. it is not convenient for him
   c. Holling's mother is on the way
   d. he does not know Holling is in the hospital

(Sequencing)

_____ 8. Right before the Hoodhood family leaves their house for the Chamber of Commerce Businessman of the Year ceremony,
   a. the living room ceiling plaster crashes in
   b. Holling flushes his carnation down the toilet
   c. Holling's sister and father get into an argument
   d. Holling's sister flushes her flower down the toilet

(Point of View)

_____ 9. Mrs. Baker describes *Romeo and Juliet* as
   a. enchanting and hypnotic
   b. tragic, beautiful, and lovely
   c. romantic, exciting, and sweet
   d. devastating, entertaining, and magical

(Main Idea and Details)

_____ 10. For Valentine's Day, Holling takes Meryl Lee to
   a. Mr. Goldman's bakery
   b. a performance of *Camelot*
   c. the Milleridge Inn restaurant
   d. a performance of *Romeo and Juliet*

(Main Idea and Details)

_____ 11. Mr. Kowalski changes his design for the new junior high by making the
   a. interior more modern
   b. exterior more modern
   c. interior more classical
   d. exterior more classical

Name _____

(Point of View)
____ 12. Whom does Holling blame for the junior high proposal dilemma?
    a. his father
    b. Meryl Lee
    c. Mr. Kowalski
    d. Mrs. Baker

(Main Idea and Details)
____ 13. Mrs. Baker receives a telegram that says her husband
    a. is severely injured
    b. is missing in action
    c. has been killed in action
    d. will come home sooner than expected

(Compare/Contrast)
B. Graphic Organizer: Using the Venn diagram below, compare and contrast the two newspaper articles about Holling.

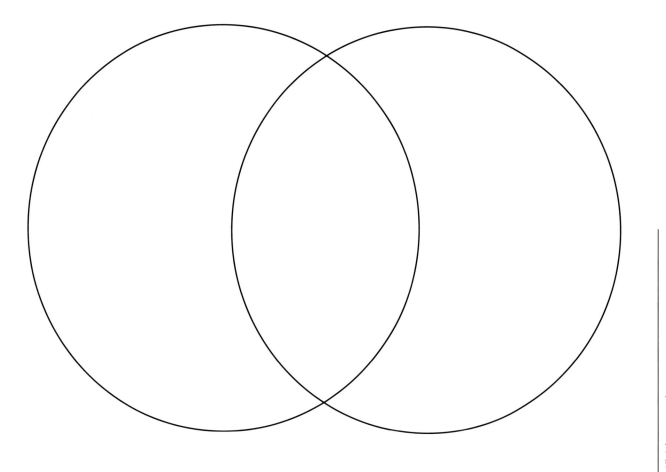

Name _____

(Literary Devices)
A. Figurative Language: Identify each item below as an example of a metaphor, a simile, or personification.

a. simile	b. metaphor	c. personification

____ 1. "…we were her garden, and she was starting to see the bulbs and seeds that she had planted in us last fall coming up."

____ 2. "running with my lungs screaming for air"

____ 3. "[The ceiling tiles] looked like sails in a full breeze."

____ 4. "On a bright blue day…when the high clouds were painted onto blue canvas…."

____ 5. "until you have ankles like cantaloupes and shins like watermelons"

(Character Analysis)
B. Identification: Fill in the correct character for each quotation.

Holling	Meryl Lee	Coach Quatrini	Mr. Hoodhood	Mrs. Baker

_____ 6. "…you dang slugs."

_____ 7. "So is that how all flower children make their judgments—so quick and easy?"

_____ 8. "I might be moving…."

_____ 9. "You think you become a man by getting a job as an architect?"

_____ 10. "A comedy is about characters who dare to know that they may choose a happy ending after all."

(Cause/Effect)
C. Cause/Effect: Identify one effect for each cause listed below.

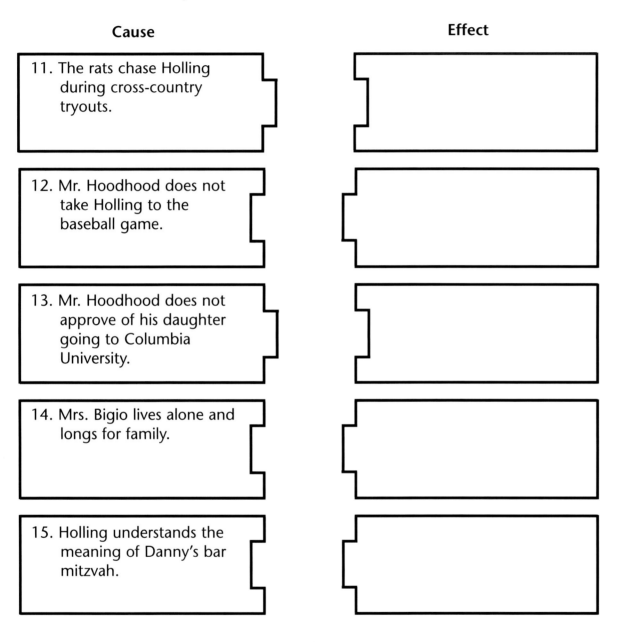

Cause   **Effect**

11. The rats chase Holling during cross-country tryouts.

12. Mr. Hoodhood does not take Holling to the baseball game.

13. Mr. Hoodhood does not approve of his daughter going to Columbia University.

14. Mrs. Bigio lives alone and longs for family.

15. Holling understands the meaning of Danny's bar mitzvah.

(Character Analysis/Drawing Conclusions)
D. Open-Ended Comprehension: On a separate sheet of paper, describe how Holling's behavior toward his father has changed from the beginning to the end of the novel, and explain why it has changed.

Name _____

(Character Analysis)

A. Identification: Match each character to the correct description.

_____ 1. Holling Hoodhood

_____ 2. Mrs. Baker

_____ 3. Mr. Hoodhood

_____ 4. Danny Hupfer

_____ 5. Meryl Lee Kowalski

_____ 6. Mai Thi Huong

_____ 7. Heather Hoodhood

_____ 8. Mr. Kowalski

_____ 9. Mr. Goldman

_____ 10. Mrs. Bigio

_____ 11. Mr. Guareschi

_____ 12. Mr. Quatrini

_____ 13. Mr. Vendleri

_____ 14. Mrs. Sidman

_____ 15. Doug Swieteck

_____ 16. Doug Swieteck's brother

a. former administrator who becomes the new principal of Camillo Junior High

b. refugee from Vietnam

c. gym and cross-country coach

d. goes on a date with Holling

e. controlling principal of Camillo Junior High

f. local bakery owner

g. seventh-grade English teacher who loves Shakespeare

h. seventh-grade boy who studies Shakespeare on Wednesdays

i. Holling's best friend; celebrates his bar mitzvah

j. Chamber of Commerce Businessman of 1967

k. owner of an architecture company that specializes in classical design

l. cafeteria worker at Camillo Junior High; loses her husband in the war

m. self-proclaimed flower child; leaves home to find herself

n. seventh-grade boy; Holling's friend; gets a black eye from his brother

o. eighth-grade bully

p. janitor at Camillo Junior High

Name _____

(Literary Devices)
B. Figurative Language: Identify each item below as an example of a metaphor, a simile, or personification.

a. simile	b. metaphor	c. personification

____ 17. "The azaleas...were half-naked and embarrassed...."

____ 18. "hamburgers...cooked as thin as a record"

____ 19. "his words hovering like the snow in the air"

____ 20. "Meryl Lee. Can the world buy such a jewel?"

____ 21. "...the daffodils were playing their trumpets...."

____ 22. "The river was a sudden ribbon of silvery light...."

(Main Idea and Details)
C. True/False: Mark each with a *T* for true or an *F* for false.

____ 23. Mr. Hoodhood expects Holling to inherit his company.

____ 24. Mrs. Bigio's husband is rescued and returns home from the war.

____ 25. Holling intentionally coats the cream puffs in chalk dust.

____ 26. Doug Swieteck's brother and his friends are about to attack Holling with snowballs when Holling is hit by a bus.

____ 27. Holling plays Ariel the Fairy in a Shakespeare production.

____ 28. Mrs. Bigio catches the rats and carries them to the basement.

____ 29. Holling Hoodhood narrates the novel in first-person point of view.

____ 30. Holling uses his savings bond to bring his sister home.

____ 31. Mr. Hoodhood takes Holling to Opening Day at Yankee Stadium.

____ 32. Mrs. Baker arranges for Holling, Doug, and Danny to meet Mickey Mantle at the school.

(Conflict/Resolution)

D. Conflict/Resolution: Explain how each conflict listed below is resolved in the novel.

Conflict	Resolution
33. Holling wants to determine his own future.	

Conflict	Resolution
34. Mrs. Baker gets angry when Holling claims she does not have much to worry about.	

Conflict	Resolution
35. Mr. Hoodhood opposes Heather's political beliefs and refuses to allow her to go to college.	

Conflict	Resolution
36. Doug Swieteck's brother wants revenge on Holling for throwing a snowball at him.	

Conflict	Resolution
37. Danny is nervous about his bar mitzvah.	

Conflict	Resolution
38. Doug Swieteck's brother is angry when Doug won't help him humiliate Holling.	

E. Essay: Choose two of the following, and write a well-developed essay for each on a separate sheet of paper. Cite specific evidence from the novel to support your responses.

(Theme/Author's Purpose)

(a) Discuss the novel's theme of "freedom over one's future." How does the author incorporate this theme using at least two characters from the story? Infer the message the author is trying to communicate to readers.

(Compare/Contrast/Support Responses)

(b) Compare and contrast at least two characters in the novel to characters in William Shakespeare's plays. Discuss whether you believe Shakespeare's works contain universal elements or not, and explain why.

(Conflict/Resolution)

(c) Describe the conflicts that are not resolved by the end of the novel. Why does the author leave these conflicts unresolved? Explain how these conflicts might be solved in the future.

(Theme/Character Analysis)

(d) Discuss how the author explores the theme that love is more powerful than war. Discuss how this theme affects at least three characters in the novel.

(Interpret Text)

(e) What does it mean if the quality of mercy is not strained? Identify at least three instances in the novel when one character shows mercy to another. In each instance, describe the effects of such behavior.

Answer Key

Activities #1–#2: Answers will vary.

Activity #3: Students will play the Vocabulary Card Game.

Activity #4: 1. rioted 2. vile 3. equation 4. quivering 5. circulate 6. presume 7. unbecoming 8. expel 9. remnants 10. mercy 11. reckon

Activity #5: 1. h 2. k 3. d 4. a 5. f 6. b 7. c 8. l 9. e 10. n 11. g 12. i 13. r 14. t 15. p 16. j 17. m 18. s 19. q 20. o

Activity #6: Crosswords will vary.

Activity #7: 1. eternal 2. arrogant 3. procedural 4. lapel 5. unsavory 6. begrudge 7. tragic 8. prosperous 9. dank 10. allotted

Activity #8: Examples for correct definitions—refuse: garbage; unalloyed: pure; underestimated: valued lowly; stance: body position; unscathed: unharmed; diction: word choice; dispense: manage without; demean: lower in dignity; vanquished: defeated; dispatch: dispose of; allusion: an indirect reference; arteries: blood vessels that carry blood to the heart; commuters: people who travel long distances; humane: enlightened; contour: molded; improper: incorrect; scaffolding: a raised platform used by builders; levitate: rise above; brittle: breakable

Activity #9: 1. a 2. b 3. b 4. a 5. a 6. b 7. a 8. c 9. c 10. c 11. b 12. a

Activity #10: A. 1. sponsored 2. climax 3. taunted 4. repellant 5. yarmulka 6. latrines 7. comedy 8. resin 9. heaved 10. nomination **B.** Sentences will vary.

Study Guide

September: 1. Camillo Junior High 2. Doug Swieteck 3. Saint Andrew Presbyterian Church 4. the "Perfect House" 5. He believes Mrs. Baker "hates [his] guts" (p. 6). 6. Mrs. Baker's family owns the Baker Sporting Emporium, which is considering hiring Hoodhood and Associates to design its new building. Mr. Hoodhood does not want Holling to ruin his firm's chance of acquiring the job. 7. *Treasure Island* 8. Camillo Junior High used to be an elementary school. 9. Holling tells her there might be a surprise inside for her, and there isn't. 10. Doug Swieteck's brother 11. She suggests that Holling retake sixth-grade mathematics. 12. Mrs. Baker's husband will soon be deployed to Vietnam.

October: 1. The Catholic Relief Agency is sponsoring her. 2. wash chalkboards, straighten dictionaries, clean various implements and areas, and put up her bulletin boards 3. the Wives of Vietnam Soldiers' gathering 4. They believe Mrs. Baker will give him a cream puff, and they think it's unfair. 5. The chalk dust from the erasers Holling is cleaning outside drifts through Mrs. Baker's windows and coats the cream puffs. 6. a bright yellow flower 7. the Chamber of Commerce Businessman of 1967 8. She wants to believe "in something bigger than just [herself]" (p. 37). 9. Shakespeare 10. the class's pet rats 11. Her husband gave them to her. 12. They climb through the radiators and into the walls of the school. 13. *The Merchant of Venice* 14. Shylock

November: 1. Some of the ceiling plaster comes down. 2. the Caliban curses 3. "*Toads, beetles, bats, light on you*" (p. 51)! 4. soprano 5. She says Meryl Lee is flirting with Holling. 6. his classmates' death threats toward him 7. Holling's father gets the Baker Sporting Emporium contract. 8. a boy who knows Shakespeare 9. $2.45 10. Sycorax and Caliban eat them while the class is at recess. 11. yellow tights with white feathers on the seat 12. She replaces his ruined cream puffs. 13. help a person grow 14. He was killed in the Vietnam War.

December: 1. a Christmas tree and a menorah 2. He thinks it might put him in favor with Mr. Goldman for a future job. 3. Mickey Mantle 4. Holling's performance in *The Tempest* 5. They are at home watching the Bing Crosby Christmas special on television. 6. They stand while crying and clapping for him. 7. He feels bad for Holling because it is freezing outside. 8. a baseball 9. because of Holling's costume 10. Danny gives his autographed ball back to Mantle and calls him a "pied ninny." 11. He remembers when she came into Mrs. Baker's room and cried after her husband died. 12. Mai Thi is from Vietnam, and Mrs. Bigio is still grieving over her husband's death in Vietnam. 13. a new baseball and baseball mitt 14. They arrange for the boys to meet the New York Yankees players Joe Pepitone and Horace Clarke.

January: 1. Holling's as Ariel the Fairy 2. He refused to help his brother cut out Holling's picture in the newspaper to post all over the school. 3. in Holling's sister's high school 4. the new junior high school contract 5. She doesn't want anything bad to happen to him. 6. that people are made for more than power and personal desires and that love is stronger than hatred 7. He doesn't want the students to miss test preparation for the New York State Standardized Achievement Tests. 8. The electricity is out. 9. Mrs. Baker 10. Doug Swieteck's brother 11. Doug Sweiteck's brother and some eighth graders 12. He pushes his sister out of the way so she won't get hit. 13. Mrs. Baker and Mr. Guareschi 14. pictures of Holling rescuing his sister

February: 1. a flower on their clothes 2. The newly repaired ceiling in the living room crashes down, causing further damage. 3. the bulging ceiling tiles 4. "tragic and beautiful and lovely" (p. 134) 5. Meryl Lee 6. "modern" 7. to a restaurant called Milleridge Inn and to see *Camelot* 8. "how much [he gives] her of [himself]" (p. 141) 9. two tickets to see *Romeo and Juliet* 10. "classical" 11. He made the interior modern while keeping the exterior classic. 12. He is upset because he believes Meryl Lee betrayed him. 13. Kowalski and Associates 14. His helicopter was shot down near Khesanh, and he is missing in action.

March: 1. Khesanh 2. Holling holds the trash can under the ceiling tiles as Mr. Vendleri changes the ones that are bulging. 3. on "the ides of March" (p. 162) 4. Coach Quatrini 5. He wants to prepare for cross-country tryouts, and he does not want to be home while his dad is mad at his sister. 6. She teaches him how to run better. 7. Jesse Owens 8. "Azalea" and "Chrysanthemum" 9. a silver medal for the 1956 XVIth Olympiad in Melbourne 10. "the power of goodness and honesty and faithfulness…the endurance of love" (pp. 171–172) 11. "Azalea" 12. Sycorax and Caliban fall through the ceiling. 13. Mrs. Sidman 14. "Motivation" 15. Sycorax and Caliban are chasing him. 16. fried bananas topped with a caramel sauce called *nuoc mau*

April: 1. Holling 2. "Operation Pegasus" 3. He knows he will lose and "he doesn't want to be humiliated" (p. 186). 4. her grandmother's house in Kingston 5. He is afraid of retaliation if he passes them. 6. the "California Gold Rush and You" (p. 189) project 7. Meryl Lee's house 8. noon 9. He calls his father's office, and finds out his father will be in an important meeting. 10. They take a tour of the Stadium with a few Yankees players and play baseball with them on the field. 11. They saw her compete in the 1956 Olympics. 12. the boss in charge of hiring a new architect 13. a boy named Chit 14. Columbia University; to stay home and work for his company 15. He emerges from the woods in almost last place with bloody knees. 16. Mrs. Baker tells Holling to pass them.

May: 1. It is Atomic Bomb Awareness Month. 2. Kowalski and Associates 3. a new, white Ford Mustang convertible with red leather interior 4. Chit 5. They help him practice for his bar mitzvah by listening to him and encouraging him. 6. He feels like the title refers to his father, and he does not "want to be him already" (p. 219). 7. "to survey points of local architectural interest" (p. 221) 8. light a candle and pray 9. his sister being gone 10. $44.55 11. $52 12. his parents; no 13. He is determined to bring his sister home. 14. Mr. Kowalski 15. him 16. "SWEET EYES"

June: 1. camping 2. He jumped out of the helicopter before it hit the ground, hid in the jungle, kept his wound clean, ate chocolate bars, and followed a river to a woman's house, where he stayed until he was found. 3. comedy 4. He is shot and killed. 5. Saint Adelbert's to light a candle and pray 6. They fall out during the hike to the campsite. 7. She lectures on dangerous snakes. 8. heavy rainfall 9. swim and dive in a waterfall 10. mosquitoes 11. bug spray, food to make *thit bo kho*, bowls, and utensils she picked up on the hike to the campsite 12. a home with her 13. He believes Danny has become a man, and he understands the importance and meaning of the ceremony. 14. Holling disagrees with his father about what it means to be a man. Holling believes that being a man is about choosing your own path in life. 15. Don Pedro, who stands alone at the end of *Much Ado About Nothing* 16. boxes of strawberries

Note: Responses to Activities #11–#20 will vary. Suggested responses are given where applicable.

Activity #11: Suggestions: Main Characters—Holling Hoodhood, Heather Hoodhood, Mr. and Mrs. Hoodhood, Mrs. Baker, Danny Hupfer, Mr. and Mrs. Hupfer, Meryl Lee Kowalski, Mr. Kowalski, Mai Thi Huong, Mrs. Bigio, Mr. Guareschi, Mr. Goldman, Mr. Vendleri, Mrs. Sidman, Doug Swieteck, Doug Swieteck's brother, Coach Quatrini; Setting—1967–1968; Long Island, New York; Main Conflict—Holling must survive the seventh grade, as well as decide if he wants to be an architect like his father; Summary of Major Story Events—Holling begins reading Shakespeare with Mrs. Baker. Holling obtains cream puffs for his class by agreeing to perform in a Shakespeare play. Holling meets Mickey Mantle and is denied an autograph because he is wearing tights. Mrs. Baker arranges for Holling and his friends to meet two other Yankees players. Doug Swieteck's brother posts a picture of Holling as Ariel the Fairy around the school. Holling throws a snowball at Doug Swieteck's brother. Holling saves his sister from being hit by a bus. Holling takes Meryl Lee on a date for Valentine's Day. Holling discovers Meryl Lee's father stole his own father's idea for a project. Holling and Meryl Lee fight and then reconcile. Mrs. Baker teaches Holling how to run, and he becomes the fastest runner in the school. Holling and Mrs. Baker go to a baseball game together when Holling's father does not take him. Holling's sister runs away to California. Holling helps bring his sister home. Holling and his class go camping. Mrs. Baker's husband returns from Vietnam; Climax—Holling confronts his father about what it means to be a man; Resolution of Conflict—Holling learns he can determine his own future.

Activity #12: Examples: Holling—family, friendship, freedom; Mrs. Baker—love, education, perseverance; Mr. Hoodhood—success, image, power; Meryl Lee—love, family, integrity; Danny— dignity, faith, family; Heather—love, peace, independence

Activity #13: Suggestions for Holling: honest—yes: Holling confesses to Mrs. Baker that he worries about his future; fair—yes: Holling gives Meryl Lee the benefit of the doubt after her father steals Mr. Hoodhood's design ideas; brave—yes: Holling saves his sister from being hit by a bus; kind—yes: Holling uses his savings bond money to bring his sister home; smart—yes: Holling learns Shakespeare quickly and is able to connect the plays to his own life; good friend—yes: Holling helps Danny prepare for his bar mitzvah; Answers will vary.

Activity #14: Examples: Character—Holling; Conflict—Holling is not sure if he wants to become an architect like his father expects him to; Resolution—Holling tells his father he wants to make his own choices and he doesn't believe a person's job defines them; Character—Mrs. Baker; Conflict— Mrs. Baker opposes the school's extensive atomic bomb drills; Resolution—She purposely spills spoiled apple cider on the Coat Room floor, forcing her and Holling to leave the room; Character—Heather; Conflict—Heather does not agree with her father about politics or self-expression; Resolution— Heather leaves home so she can pursue what is important to her.

Activity #15: Examples: Holling—smart, determined, well-behaved; Meryl Lee—sensitive, strong, friendly; Doug Swieteck's brother—troublemaker, mean, calculating; Mrs. Baker—intelligent, compassionate, hopeful; Danny Hupfer—loyal, fair, kind; Mr. Hoodhood—ambitious, self-centered, strong-willed

Activity #16: Answers will vary.

Activity #17: Example for Mrs. Baker: Actions/Words—Mrs. Baker teaches Holling Shakespeare; Reason—She wants to challenge him; Traits—intelligent, strong-willed, caring; Holling thinks Mrs. Baker hates him. He also assumes she has always been a teacher. Holling later likes and respects Mrs. Baker.

Activity #18: Answers will vary.

Activity #19: Suggestions: 1. Holling learns and performs Shakespeare. 2. Holling is humiliated when pictures of him in costume are posted all over the school. 3. Holling gets revenge on Doug Swieteck's brother by hitting him with a snowball. 4. Holling saves his sister from being hit by a bus. 5. Holling brings his sister home when his parents refuse. 6. Holling stands up to his father.

Activity #20: Possible Themes—love, war, reconciliation, family, coming of age, peace, hope, success, perseverance, identity, friendship; Author's Main Message—People have the ability to determine their own future; Lessons learned will vary.

Quiz #1: A. 1. Gary D. Schmidt 2. Long Island, New York in 1967 3. fiction 4. love, war, reconciliation, family, coming of age, peace, hope, success, perseverance, identity, friendship 5. Holling vs. himself; Holling vs. Mrs. Baker; Holling vs. his class; Holling's father vs. Holling's sister 6. Holling Hoodhood, Mrs. Baker, Mr. Hoodhood, Holling's sister 7. Danny Hupfer, Meryl Lee, Mai Thi, Mrs. Bigio, Doug Swieteck and his brother **B.** 8. T 9. F 10. T 11. F 12. F 13. F 14. F 15. T 16. F 17. T **C.** Responses will vary.

Quiz #2: A. 1. c 2. c 3. d 4. a 5. b 6. b 7. b 8. a 9. b 10. d 11. a 12. b 13. b **B.** Responses will vary but should include how one picture is posted around the school to humiliate Holling, and the other picture is meant to show his bravery.

Quiz #3: A. 1. b (p. 157) 2. c (p. 164) 3. a (p. 158) 4. b (p. 222) 5. a (p. 249) **B.** 6. Coach Quatrini (p. 177) 7. Mr. Hoodhood (p. 186) 8. Meryl Lee (p. 187) 9. Holling (p. 260) 10. Mrs. Baker (p. 262) **C.** Answers will vary. Suggestions: 11. Holling makes the varsity team and sets a new record for the three-mile run for a Long Island school. 12. Mrs. Baker takes Holling to the baseball game. 13. Holling's sister leaves home for California with Chit. 14. Mrs. Bigio asks Mai Thi to live with her. 15. Holling argues with his father about what it means to be a man. **D.** Responses will vary.

Novel Test
A. 1. h 2. g 3. j 4. i 5. d 6. b 7. m 8. k 9. f 10. l 11. e 12. c 13. p 14. a 15. n 16. o **B.** 17. c (p. 49) 18. a (p. 94) 19. a (p. 122) 20. b (p. 261) 21. c (p. 181) 22. b (p. 257) **C.** 23. T 24. F 25. F 26. T 27. T 28. F 29. T 30. T 31. F 32. F **D.** Answers will vary. Suggestions: 33. Holling stands up to his father about the definition of a man and expresses his desire to choose his own career. 34. Mrs. Baker forgives Holling after he is hit by a bus. 35. Heather leaves home for California to find herself. 36. Doug Swieteck's brother and his friends wait after school to hit Holling with snowballs, but Holling is hit by a bus before they exact revenge. 37. Holling, Meryl Lee, and Mai Thi help Danny practice, and he has a successful, meaningful ceremony. 38. Doug Swieteck's brother punches Doug in the face, resulting in a black eye for Doug. **E.** Essays will vary. Refer to the scoring rubric on page 44 of this guide.

Linking Novel Units® Student Packets to National and State Reading Assessments

During the past several years, an increasing number of students have faced some form of state-mandated competency testing in reading. Many states now administer state-developed assessments to measure the skills and knowledge emphasized in their particular reading curriculum. This Novel Units® guide includes open-ended comprehension questions that correlate with state-mandated reading assessments. The rubric below provides important information for evaluating responses to open-ended comprehension questions. Teachers may also use scoring rubrics provided for their own state's competency test.

Scoring Rubric for Open-Ended Items

3-Exemplary	Thorough, complete ideas/information Clear organization throughout Logical reasoning/conclusions Thorough understanding of reading task Accurate, complete response
2-Sufficient	Many relevant ideas/pieces of information Clear organization throughout most of response Minor problems in logical reasoning/conclusions General understanding of reading task Generally accurate and complete response
1-Partially Sufficient	Minimally relevant ideas/information Obvious gaps in organization Obvious problems in logical reasoning/conclusions Minimal understanding of reading task Inaccuracies/incomplete response
0-Insufficient	Irrelevant ideas/information No coherent organization Major problems in logical reasoning/conclusions Little or no understanding of reading task Generally inaccurate/incomplete response